THIS BOOK IS

. . . . Coggo . . . .

THE WORLD'S MOST IDIOTIC/SEXY/UGLY/ROMANTIC/SMELLY/GORGEOUS/CHARMING/FAT/USELESS/VIRGOAN
(Can't decide)

YOURS IN DISGUST/LOTS OF LOVE

BEST WISHES . . . . Liz + Jim Brooko . . . .

P.S. PLEASE TAKE NOTE OF PAGE(S)

. . . . 44 . . . .

THE VIRGO BOOK

A CORGI BOOK 0 552 12321 8

First publication in Great Britain
PRINTING HISTORY
Corgi edition published 1983
Corgi edition reissued 1984
Corgi edition reprinted 1985

Corgi Books are published by Transworld Publishers Ltd., Century House, 61-63 Uxbridge Road, Ealing, London W5 5SA, in Australia by Transworld Publishers (Aust.) Pty. Ltd., 26 Harley Crescent, Condell Park, NSW 2200, and in New Zealand by Transworld Publishers (N.Z.) Ltd., Cnr. Moselle and Waipareira Avenues, Henderson, Auckland.

Made and printed in Great Britain by the
Guernsey Press Co. Ltd., Guernsey, Channel Islands.

THE VIRGO BOOK

BY

IAN HEATH

VIRGO

AUGUST 22 – SEPTEMBER 22

SIXTH SIGN OF THE ZODIAC

SYMBOL : THE MAIDEN

RULING PLANET : MERCURY

COLOURS : YELLOW, GREY

GEM : ONYX

NUMBER : FIVE

DAY : WEDNESDAY

METAL : ANTIMONY

FLOWER : LAVENDER

ZZZZZZZZ

The VIRGOAN at work........

.............IS SLOW...................

..............HONEST..................

...... CAN BE TOUCHY ....

.....WILL DO ANYTHING..............

........DRESSES SMARTLY............

..........IS HARD-HEADED............

......DELEGATES WELL..............

...NEVER TIRES OF PUBLIC DUTY......

.....IS SOMETIMES CARELESS..........

.... AND ADVENTUROUS.

FINANCIAL
TIMES
The VIRGOAN finds success as...

.....A DOORMAN..................

POPCORN PACKER

......SECURITY GUARD...................

.......RESEARCH CHEMIST..........

........TREE-SURGEON..................

........DENTAL MECHANIC............

..... OR CAR SALESMAN.

The VIRGOAN at home..............

.......IS STRICT.........................

....LIKES INTELLIGENT FRIENDS....

..... MAKES WINE ....

......IS AN OBSERVER..............

....NOT A GOOD LISTENER.......

.....A USELESS GARDENER.......

.....A DEDICATED COOK..............

A GOSSIP..........................

.....LIKES READING STORIES.......

....AND WON'T PAY BILLS.

The VIRGOAN likes........

........PRESSED FLOWERS.........

..........FLYING.....................

......DISCUSSING POLITICS..........

......HOT, SANDY PLACES............

HOT BATHS..........................

. . . . AND CHOCOLATE MOUSSE.

The
VIRGOAN
dislikes..............

..... MAKING SPEECHES ....

RECEIVING BILLS

......LOUD NOISES..................

......MAKING DECISIONS..........

.......TAPIOCA PUDDING............

.....AND FOOTBALL.

The
VIRGOAN
in love........................

......ANALYSES PARTNER...........

.....CAN BE JEALOUS..................

........IS VERY UNSURE...............

....RESISTS SEDUCTIVE ADVANCES....

.....IS VERY SELF-CENTRED...........

.....PLAYS HARD TO GET............

....DOES NOT WANT TO DOMINATE...

........IS PASSIONATE..................

FAITHFUL

....AND POSSESSIVE.

VIRGOAN AND PARTNER

HEART RATINGS

♥♥♥♥♥ WOWEE!!
♥♥♥♥ GREAT, BUT NOT 'IT'
♥♥♥ O.K. – COULD BE FUN
♥♥ FORGET IT
♥ RUN THE OTHER WAY—FAST!

CAPRICORN TAURUS

LIBRA SCORPIO CANCER
LEO

SAGITTARIUS VIRGO

PISCES GEMINI

AQUARIUS ARIES

VIRGO PEOPLE

PETER SELLERS : LEO TOLSTOY
MAURICE CHEVALIER : TWIGGY
LAUREN BACALL : JESSE JAMES
MICKEY MOUSE : D.H. LAWRENCE

RAY CHARLES : H. G. WELLS
SOPHIA LOREN : ELLIOTT GOULD
O. HENRY : QUEEN ELIZABETH I
GRETA GARBO : INGRID BERGMAN
ROALD DAHL : SIR HARRY SECOMBE
SIR JOHN BETJEMAN
SEAN CONNERY : ZANDRA RHODES
STIRLING MOSS : J. B. PRIESTLEY
SIR PETER SCOTT : TOM WATSON
GENE KELLY : BROOK BENTON
SIR DONALD BRADMAN